CONWY MULBERRY HARBOUR

Contents

Conwy Mulberry Harbour

Mark Hughes

ISBN: 0-86381-757-2

Cover design: Sian Parri

First published in 2001 by
Gwasg Carreg Gwalch, 12 Iard yr Orsaf, Llanrwst, Wales LL26 0EH
✆ 01492 642031 🖷 01492 641502
✉ books@carreg-gwalch.co.uk   Website: www.carreg-gwalch.co.uk

*I am grateful for various encouragements and assistances offered
by Rosemary Hughes, David Birch, Les Williams, Geoffrey Stone,
Linda Stone, Keith Walker and Dylan Parri.*

To Pam, Ben, Helen and Lloyd.

INTRODUCTION

Britain and France suffered enormously because of the First World War, the one that was supposed to put an end to all such barbarity. The League of Nations was created to achieve this very end but political naivety linked to social and economic conditions that would have tested any civilisation, destabilised all attempts to engineer a lasting peace. Germany suffered more than any country, mostly because of the punitive nature of the Treaty of Versailles, but quickly redeveloped her forces. The Allies having stripped her of all armaments, most of which were obsolete in any case, meant that Germany was able to rebuild and rearm with modern and advanced equipment. Britain and France at the same time allowed severe deterioration to set in.

By the time that Britain and France realised that rearming was the only means of combating the new, and more menacing than ever before, Teutonic war machine, it was too late. Czechoslovakia was the first to experience a method of waging war that quickly became familiar to the whole of Europe as *Blitzkrieg*, in March 1939. Both the other European powers were driven into a corner from which there was no escape. They announced their support for Poland and when invasion followed on 1 September 1939, the inevitable outcome was to declare war on Germany two days later. Poland however was left high and dry in the face of a German army that brought about the country's collapse in less than a month.

There then ensued a state of phoney war, or *twilight war* as Winston Churchill put it, during which Britain and France continued their frantic efforts to rearm. They were given six months before Germany annexed Norway and Denmark in quick succession in April 1940. The following month, British and French forces came face to face with the German fighting machine for the first time, and were found severely wanting. France surrendered within six very short weeks and the British army, with a large contingent of French, was evacuated from Dunkirk. They were forced to leave most of the military hardware behind on the beach, but the propaganda, engineered out of what was in reality a humiliating defeat, successfully portrayed it as a great victory in that so many lives were saved.

Even Hitler was apparently surprised by the capitulation. His reaction however was to delay a sea-borne invasion of Britain, to allow the Luftwaffe to soften British resistance. The Royal Air Force however was made of stern stuff and Germany suffered a huge setback in losing what became known as the Battle of Britain. In frustration, attention was turned to Russia who could be beaten before attending once and for all to Britain. As it turned out, Russia was made of even sterner stuff than the RAF. German commanders, like their French counterparts almost a century and a half earlier, did not take the all-important element of a full-blown Russian winter into consideration. Nor did they calculate for the size and sheer determination of the Russian army, especially one that had its back to the wall. The Germans were at the gates of Moscow by December 1941, but that was the furthest they got.

By the time that Japan brought the sleeping giant of America into the war, the German army, which until then had seemed invincible, was floundering about without suitable equipment in one of the most inhospitable winters on earth. What was supposed to be a glorious victory turned, for the Germans, into the bitterest front in what was by now a global war. By mid to late 1942 the war was steadily but surely turning over to the Allies. America defeated the Japanese at the Battle of Medway; El Alamein proved decisive for Hitler and Mussolini in North Africa. With the huge resources of America at last directed towards Europe, attacks on the continental mainland began. Italy was taken out of the war by September 1943 as Allied forces began the slow and painful task of pushing the Germans northwards whilst the Russians were forcing them back on the eastern front.

Plans were afoot for a combined British/American force to invade across the English Channel and there was an immense build-up of troops, air and naval power in Britain. Allied commanders knew that the Normandy coast was to be the site of savage, uncompromising warfare because German troops and artillery would do absolutely anything to hold this front. What was clear to the staff at Combined Operations was that a naval blockade could not oust the Germans, and that air power alone would not be enough to break their resistance. Landing troops and supplies would be imperative if an invasion was to succeed, as unsuccessful attacks on French ports had shown that the Germans were well able to defend themselves.

All agreed that sheltered water had to be provided artificially and that special berthing facilities would be necessary within an artificial harbour. Due to the need for secrecy, it was decided to construct the components of a floating harbour in Britain, which would then be towed across the Channel and installed off the occupied French beaches. Chiefs of Staff decided that they would be based on a principle comprising of three units, all built on a huge scale.

1. Breakwaters:
Ships needed calm water within the harbours to discharge their loads, and the only way of providing this was through constructing breakwaters. These would consist of three elements. The most important would be a series of immense reinforced concrete caissons (airtight cases), open at the bottom to seawater that could be raised and lowered by removing or adding seawater as necessary and be called PHOENIX. They would be very costly to produce and therefore BLOCKSHIPS could be sunk to provide additional sheltered water. Outside of these, giant steel booms built in the shape of a crucifix and called BOMBARDONS would give further protection.

2. Pierheads:
These floating quays were to be set within the harbour to provide ships with stable platforms onto which to discharge their cargoes.

3. Floating Roadways:
When supplies had been discharged onto the pierheads, they then needed to be transported onto the beaches. Floating roadways were seen as the answer.

Throughout the United Kingdom forty-five thousand personnel from over three hundred firms built twenty three pierheads, two hundred and twelve caissons, ten miles (16km) of floating roadway as well as other components. By the end of October 1944, 25% of supplies, 20% of reinforcements and 15% of the vehicles that the army needed were landed through British built Mulberry Harbours, which contributed greatly to the winning of the War.

Not many Conwy people, in 1942, 1945 and certainly not in 2001, knew of the contribution the town made to the winning of the Second World War. The area near the town known as the Morfa was transformed into a huge building site where prototypes were initially constructed followed by some of the chosen components of the Mulberry Harbours. Between 1942 and the end of 1944, nearly a thousand men, some from Conwy but many also from other parts of Britain, worked tirelessly under the direction of Hugh Iorys Hughes, a locally born man who was an innovative and successful civil engineer.

CHAPTER 1

The idea of using artificial ports to supply an invading force may be taken back to the First World War when, ten days before he joined Lloyd George's Government as Minster of Munitions in 1917, Winston Churchill drafted a detailed military paper outlining the capture of two occupied Frisian Islands, Borkum and Sylt, lying off the Dutch and Danish coasts. His plan described the construction of an artificial island or harbour off Horn Reef using a number of flat-bottomed barges or caissons, measuring some 120 feet (37m) by 80 feet (23m) by 40 feet (12m). The units would be adaptable to various water depths and built of concrete for reasons of economy. They were to be prepared in the Humber, at Harwich, the Wash, at Medway and on the Thames, before being towed to the artificial island whilst empty and then sunk at specific sites by gradually adding sand. Churchill's plan was to create a torpedo and weatherproof harbour in the open sea, with regular pens for destroyers and submarines, and alighting platforms for planes. Other sinkable structures were also proposed by Churchill which were to be towed in a similar fashion, but constructed so as to provide store rooms, oil tanks or living accommodation as required.

Although Churchill's report was not published, this work is generally believed to be the precursor of the Mulberry Harbours, one of the most important engineering plans of the Second World War. Early in 1941, Hugh Iorys Hughes, a successful London based Welsh civil engineer, also had the idea of using a harbour to provide protection and supplies for an invading force. He sent his ideas to a department of the War Office that dealt with the more 'unusual' plans and, like many others, it was shelved. It was however brought to the attention of a higher authority following a telephone call from Hughes's brother Siôr; a Naval Commander, and it was duly considered.

On 4 June 1940, Winston Churchill impressed on the members of the House of Commons that, although Dunkirk had represented a failure, it had proved highly successful in that so many troops were rescued. He stressed that there should be no thought of capitulation to the Germans and that the fight would continue to the end. For a period of more than a year after Dunkirk, little thought was given to invading occupied France. The strategy was primarily defensive and aimed at keeping sea lanes open, protecting the Middle East, blockading the occupied coast and developing relations with resistance groups. To the dismay and astonishment of the Germans, the Luftwaffe was defeated by the R.A.F in the Battle of Britain. The British and Canadian military planners were now more confident that there would not be an attack on Britain in the winter months, and two precursory large scale attacks on the French ports of Saint-Nazaire and Dieppe were put into operation. The result however was disastrous with huge Canadian losses sustained due to a lack of air protection, and the heavy firepower and armoured equipment of the enemy. This caused a decision to the effect that a successful invasion would have to be undertaken over open beaches via an artificial port. The would-be port was randomly code named Mulberry Harbours.

Normandy in Northern France, with its wide, flat and sandy beaches and relative closeness to Britain, was chosen as the intended invasion point. It was calculated that two harbours would be required to land enough men and adequate supplies in the shortest possible time. Mulberry A was to supply the two beaches code-named Omaha and Utah in the American sector, whilst Mulberry B would do the same for the 'British' beaches of Gold, Juno, and Sword.

Early in 1941, a government section code named Transportation 5 (Tn5), was formed by Major General D.J. McMullen and given the responsibility for port engineering, repair and maintenance. Under the command of civil engineer Bruce White, the section's first task was to construct two military ports at Gare Loch, north of Greenock and the Firth of Clyde near Glasgow. These were used as deep-water berths for ships and became the first point of entry into Britain for American forces, leaving the ports on the western coast further south free for other military vessels.

British and American forces were not ready to invade occupied Europe in 1943 and agreed that the earliest an invasion could be launched was May of 1944. The following months saw many meetings between the British and Americans to discuss the options for providing calm waters for the harbours. These included suggestions such as sinking ships on site, although it was already known that ships had the wrong profile to form a line of resistance, and were prone to breaking up across the engine room. The one advantage was that they were able to move under their own power to the required station. The most satisfactory suggestion was for the use of *Caissons*, which were large watertight cases open at the bottom and kept afloat, or otherwise, by the amount of compressed air pumped in, or let out. This method had been successfully used before and was considered satisfactory. An idea that caused a request for a report on its efficiency was that of concrete pontoons and balloon equipment, but such floating devices were known to be difficult to moor. Another suggestion was the use of floating barriers (known first as 'Lie-low', later shortened to Lilo) that were invented by Robert Lochner, head of the Heavy Engineering section of the Department of Miscellaneous Weapon Development in the Admiralty. A test was ordered to assess what affect a line of collapsible canvas floating breakwaters had on wave size reduction. The harbours would have to be larger than the port of Dover, which had taken seven years to complete in the safety of peace time. It was decided that it would be based on a principle combining Breakwaters, Pierheads and floating Roadways and the Prime Minister instructed his Chief of Combined Operations, Admiral Lord Mountbatten, to provide the plans. He soon discovered however that the huge quantity of floating equipment was beyond the capability of his relatively small department and contracted the War Office to construct and run the operational aspects of the venture.

The first plans Mountbatten submitted gave a time limit of seven months for completion, resulting in further requirements being discussed on 9 August 1943. These included the need to be able to place the structures within a maximum of four days. It was also deemed necessary to have a sufficient depth of sea to accommodate 22 feet (6.7m) of draught for sea vessels.

Mountbatten now had the problem of convincing the British

Chiefs of Staff that the proposals for the allied invasion, Codename Overlord; could work over open beaches using an artificial harbour. A conference involving British and American military planners was arranged in North America for August 1943 to discuss the invasion plans, and the British contingent would have to be on his side before they got to Canada. On the sea passage to the conference aboard the liner *Queen Mary*, Mountbatten asked his companions to gather in one of the ship's bathrooms where he and his staff had arranged a lecture that was to prove invaluable. Here the physician Professor J.D. Bernal, one of Mountbatten's closest advisors, gave a demonstration. Admiral Sir Dudley Pound stationed himself on the lavatory seat and asked his bewildered colleagues to imagine the shallow end of the bath as a beachhead. Professor Bernal then floated twenty 'paper' ships in the bath and requested Lt-Cdr Grant to produce 'waves' using the back of a brush. Nobody was surprised as the 'fleet' sank. He retrieved the sunken ships and this time placed them within the confines of an inflated Mae West lifebelt. The artificial waves were produced again, but this time the ships remained afloat due to the protection provided within the lifebelt. It was upon such a simple exhibition that the need for sheltered water was sold.

At the meeting in Quebec the larger proportion of American naval and military engineers needed convincing that floating pierheads and caisson breakwaters could work successfully in the harbour. The Admiralty, who had been developing floating breakwaters, took no time in flying Tn5 engineers across the Atlantic for another meeting in Washington. Having seen films and working models, the Combined Chiefs of Staff approved the proposals for the floating harbours and, due to the huge distances involved in crossing the Atlantic, decided that all the construction work would be done in Britain.

The first components to be considered were the 2¼ miles (3.6km) of concrete caissons that were required, but work would forge ahead simultaneously on the development of the breakwaters, pierheads and floating roadways. The rigours of three years of war had strained productivity to the limit, and such essential commodities as steel were in short supply. There were huge difficulties to be encountered in building such an immense structure in seven months.

The British Chiefs of staff decided that Sir Harold Wernher be given the job of Co-ordinator of Ministry and Service Facilities, to oversee the preparation of the south coast for launching the invasion. He was to act as liaison between all the British and American departments concerned with the development of ports, sheltered anchorages and landing facilities and to also ensure that the Mulberry programme requirements were met and delivered on time.

Before the Quebec meeting, the Chief of Staff had decided that the Admiralty would be responsible for sheltered anchorages, floating equipment and block ships. The War Office was to be responsible for the development of all other port and unloading equipment. After the meeting however, these arrangements were changed. The War Office was given the responsibility for designing the caissons and supervising the development of pierheads and piers, whilst the Admiralty was to go ahead with the floating breakwaters. All was not to go as well as expected. The Admiralty showed little response to even reasonable requests and were displeased by Tn5 taking responsibility for the harbour layout. For reasons of security Tn5 would not divulge what their port engineers were preparing and senior staff at the Admiralty were particularly worried about berthing facilities, navigational guide set-up and the time it would take to complete the harbour installation once it had arrived in French waters. The matter was finally resolved at a Christmas Day meeting between the Admirals, Army supply and Transport Officers. All agreed that the Admiralty should be responsible for towing all the components across the Channel, as well as the layout and siting of the harbours. They were also to survey the harbour sites, position the breakwaters and make the navigational channels and moorings. The War Office would design and build the caissons and store them until required for towing, and provide protection from air attack. The discharge facility, construction and installation were also placed under their control.

The decision was finally and officially made that Normandy

would be the entry point into France. Work was already underway on securing detailed information about the nature of the French shoreline, and civil engineers were already involved in producing plans and prototypes of the required floating equipment. Iorys Hughes, who had contacted the War Office with his ideas at an earlier date, was one of the experts that had received a request from the Prime Minister's office.

CHAPTER 2

The Allied Chiefs of Staff wanted to ensure that the British coastline was in the most satisfactory condition to enable effective embarkation. They also had a far more difficult and dangerous requirement in that precise information be obtained about the nature of the beaches and surrounding area at the proposed landing sites in France.

The task of surveying the area between Plymouth and Glasgow was entrusted to Colonel Ian McKillop and was huge in scale and minute in detail. The calculations revealed that one hundred and seventy-one embarkation points were needed for Landing Craft for Tanks (LCTs) and Landing Ships for Tanks (LSTs). Maintenance depots, accommodation for crews and their provisions, storage for oil and water, as well as lighting facilities were required at the sites. Roads were widened to some of the areas, whilst new ones were laid to others.

The responsibility for supervising the construction of thirty-six embarkation points on the south coast of England was given to Sir Harold Wernher, co-ordinator of the Ministry and Service Facility. He was assisted by a committee formed under the command of the Engineer in Chief of the Admiralty. A very tight time limit of three months was given for the completion of the initial reconnaissance. The first major problem that the committee encountered was a means of moving tanks and other vehicles across the beaches between low and high tide. Of the many valuable suggestions that were submitted, it was that of Colonel Vassal Steer-Webster, serving on the staff of the Director of Transportation of the War Office, that was considered most likely to succeed. His idea involved utilising four thousand concrete mattresses, each measuring 3ft.4in by 2ft. by 5in (1m x 60cm x 12.7cm) and weighing 350lbs (160kg) each. They were to be reinforced with wire and to cover an area of 28,000 square feet (9744m sq).

Wernher decided that the Steer-Webster invention should be tested. The experimental work was entrusted to Lt-Cmdr Earl Beatty and following some positive test results, it was decided that there should be no delay in their large-scale construction. Initially thirty-six were built, with an additional sixty-six LST and one hundred and seventy-one LCT embarkation points made in the next two years at various sites along the British coastline. A handful of LSTs that had been cut in two to facilitate their transportation across the Atlantic from America on tankers, arrived in Britain where they were welded together at around the time that the North African landings were completed.

As the embarkation point problem had been overcome, and with the promise of additional transportation vessels from America, it was unanimously agreed that the time had arrived to consider the nature of the French coastline. The intended invasion points on the northern coast of France were known to be rocky in nature and poorly provided with paths from the beaches landwards. Studies had also revealed that there was a difference of 27 feet (8.2m) between high and low water marks, and that unpredictable swirling currents could be encountered.

As there were few official photographs available of the French coastline, the public was asked to send in snap-shots and postcards of the area. An influx of pictures of every French city, town and village on the coast was received, and an all angle record of Arromanche was subsequently formed.

Professor Bernard, Chief Scientific Officer to Combined Operations, along with Sir Malcolm Campbell who had performed work on the bearing capacities of sand for his record breaking land speed records in *Bluebird*, were asked to read up on the geological history of the Normandy beaches. At the British Museum they studied various documents and by chance came upon the *Roman de Rou*, the account of William the Conqueror's crossing at low tide of the Grand Rue, now called La Baie des Ryes. Much useful information was gleamed from this paper.

As with many previous wartime plans, all the information was collated from the various sources and a model room of the proposed landing area was deemed necessary. This is why, in room 474 of the Great Metropole Hotel in Northumberland Avenue, London, the War Office had expert modellers build a scale model of the Normandy beaches near the towns of Arromanche, Port-en-Bessin and Ryes as well as the cliffs, houses and roads. Steer-Webster and Major Beckett, the inventor of the kite anchor, were also instructed to assemble a panel of experimenters at Cairnryan on Loch Ryan, north of Stanraer in Scotland. Here the information that was collected from air reconnaissance, submarine survey and landing parties was translated into a ' life size' reproduction of the beaches that it was hoped the men and supplies would have to cross in the event of a successful invasion.

The most detailed information was received from Captain Nigel Willmott's collecting unit, the Combined Operations Pilotage Party (C.O.P.P.). This unit, along with the Special Boat Squadron (S.B.S.) which was originally an army unit born of No. 8 Commando, had its origins in Egypt in early 1941 when a small operation was mounted to carry out a series of reconnaissances of beaches on the Italian held Greek island of Rhodes. The team composed of Lt-Cmdr Nigel Willmott, Lieut Roger Courtney and Lance Corporal J. B. Sherwood. Both Courtney and Sherwood were members of the Folbot Section, a unit formed by Courtney following a direct order from the Chief of Combined Operations, Admiral Sir Roger Keyes, famous from the raid on Zeebrugge in the First World War.

Sherwood, who now lives in Chester, had volunteered for the Commandos soon after Dunkirk. He was accepted and found himself on No. 8 Commando, then in Inverary in Scotland and eventually on Arran Island on the Clyde. Here by chance, he heard that a canoeing unit was being formed and asked to join it. He was interviewed by Roger Courtney and was accepted following the disclosure that he had owned a two-seater canoe whilst working in Dublin, and had used it on the open sea.

Concentrated training took place at Arran until the twelve other ranks and two N.C.O's were proficient at canoe handling. Sir Roger Keyes visited Arran and was greatly impressed with what he saw. The new unit trained day and night in canoe handling, reconnaissance, compass work and general field craft. The departure date for Egypt was set for 1 February 1941 and all the members of the unit given two weeks leave before setting off. The unit was moved and its Headquarters set up at a commandeered guesthouse, Ingledene, at Sannox on the East coast of Scotland. It was from here that they sailed for Egypt.

On the voyage, the small, fast convoy of three ships was attached to Layforce, which was itself comprised of the 2nd, 8th and 11th Scottish Commandos, and escorted by the Royal Navy ships *H.M.S Glengyle*, *Glennoy* and *Glenearn* via the Cape of Good Hope. Shortly after arriving in Egypt, Sherwood was told by Courtney to accompany him and Willmott on a secret operation. Several night exercises were carried out off the shores of the Suez Canal to determine how long a folbot could remain unseen as it approached the shoreline. They were surprised as to how near their craft could get to the beach, even with observers in position who knew what to expect and were actively seeking them.

Willmott, Courtney and Sherwood were transported to Rhodes with two folbots in *H.M. Submarine Triumph*. Sherwood was put in charge of the canoes and his job was to assist in launching them from the submarine with the two officers on board, and then acting as a back up should anything go wrong. Held in place by Sherwood and some sailors from the submarine, Willmott and Courtney entered the calm water from the starboard fore-plane. To ensure their safe return to the submarine, they were provided with an infrared signalling lamp, the signal being picked up by a receiver. This particular operation went without any mishaps and the two officers were able to report about shore conditions that would be suitable for landing craft to operate. No mines were found. Thus was witnessed the birth of C.O.P.P and the S.B.S. Following the success of this operation, both units went their separate ways and grew to fame as the War progressed and their operations multiplied.

The first date to be chosen for the reconnaissance of the French beaches was New Years Eve 1943. Major Logan Scott-Bowden of the Royal Engineers, who was 24 years of age, had until that time been unaware that Normandy would be the D-Day landing site. His group travelled by motor torpedo boat across the Channel in less than favourable weather. To their surprise, the lighthouse on the high ground near Luc-sur-Mer was still operating, and it was near here that they transferred to a hydrographical survey craft, whilst still some distance from the shore. They travelled 2 miles (3.2km) landwards from where, still outside the breakwaters, Scott-Bowden and Sergeant Bruce Ogden-Smith swam ashore. They wore primitive old-fashioned diving suits and were equipped with wrist compasses, watches, torches and other essential equipment that would be needed for the task in hand. Each man carried a dozen long tubes, numbered on top in phosphorus, in a bandolier on their backs. The idea was to take various samples from different parts of the beach and record the identification of the sites on waterproof tablets.

Aiming for a point a little over half a mile (1 km) west of Luc-sur-Mer, the strong current carried them east towards the village where, although screened by the lighthouse beam, they moved ashore and crawled back along the beach keeping below the high water mark. They took samples from the various locations, filling eight of the tubes. The breakers proved difficult to beat on their return from the beach, and it took three attempts to swim out to the rendezvous point before they were successful. Here they flashed their torches and contacted the rescue craft, commanded by Lt-Cmdr Nigel Willmott of the Royal Navy. Both men were totally exhausted by the time boarded, but the reconnaissance had been a complete success with a variety of samples of peat, sand, mud and shingle collected. They were also able to report on possible sitings of minefields.

Approximately one month later a midget submarine, *X20*, under the command of Lieut K. Hudspeth (DSC and 2 Bars) was the means of transport across the Channel. This time the other members of the crew included Commander Willmott, Lieut Ensor (later killed in diving practice), Lt-Cmdr Clarke and Major Scott-Bowden, along with an additional artificer.

Lieut Carl Brunning of the *Darthema* towed the submarine halfway across a 2 mile (3.2km) stretch of the Channel, which had been previously cleared by order of the Commander in Charge in Portsmouth. No aircraft were allowed to fly over the area and no Allied ships on night patrol were allowed to enter it. On this occasion they headed for a point to the west of Port-en-Bessin and Vierville. They sighted the coast at 4.00a.m and took positional bearings. Submerged and travelling unseen at three knots and remaining some distance from the shore, they surfaced for three to four hours to recharge the vessel's batteries. When the time was right, they approached the beach whilst using a sounding pole every 100 yards (90m). They took notes on the currents and tidal streams and purposely grounded the vessel. They then carried out as detailed a survey as possible under such conditions, which was again to prove vital to the model makers in London.

The next operation, three weeks later in a full dark period, was to one of the proposed American beaches (Omaha). The submarine and its crew was towed by trawler this time and the same men, Scott-Bowden, Skipper and engineer; Willmott and Ogden-Smith, again went through the routine of resurfacing to recharge the batteries. They had in the meantime developed a technique for bottoming their vessel that would help them take bearings on what they viewed through the periscope. Using this method they were able to define items such as the extent of the fortifications and large concrete constructions that were not visible from air reconnaissance. As darkness drew in, they left the submarine approximately 300 yards (270m) from the beach and swam ashore. They tested the firmness of the beaches by pushing augers into the soft ground. They had planned to test one side of the beach on one night and the other the next. On the first night they worked unhampered, but the next foray proved more difficult as the sea was calm, and observers could far more easily see them. On this occasion, samples of pebbles and sand were taken from the beach.

Darthema kept patrol in the waters of northern France for a week and waited for a signal from the crew of X20. No call for help was received and at the end of the week the submarine appeared back in Britain having made her own way back, with all the crew and landing party intact. Due to the success of the surveys no further full-scale operations were needed until the invasion preparations had been made.

In room 473 of the Great Metropole Hotel, there now lay one of the most prized secrets of the Second World War. Here was a centimetre by centimetre scale model of the Normandy beaches, with the towns of Arromanche, Port-en-Bessin and Ryes built to scale. Another duplicate model room was set up in the Prime Minister's room in the War Cabinet Offices. Both model rooms were out of bounds to all, bar an exclusive few. One honoured guest was the King who brought along his two small daughters. He visited more frequently as the models reached completion and, as D-Day approached, the attraction of the developing model room gave him the opportunity see the information converted into three-dimensional form by Sika Lancaster and others.

CHAPTER 3

The Allied raid on Tunis on 6 May 1943 was a great success and played a large part in convincing Hitler that the Allied invading mainland Europe was inevitable. He believed that France, the nearest occupied country to Britain, would be the chosen site, but ignored his generals' warnings that the barren lands of Normandy could be at risk. His first instinct was that an attack would be targeted at one of the major ports, such as Pas de Calais.

Those French coastal areas considered likely invasion points were, however, given top priority for defence. Approximately a quarter of a million conscript workers and as many troops were recruited to work on the construction of what was known as the *Festunga Europa*; or *Atlantic Wall*, a giant system of defensive fortifications running from Norway to Spain. This huge structure was to be supported by an array of subsidiary defences, including mine fields and strong points, around which artillery would be positioned and protected in concrete housing.

The construction of the wall was going well until delays forced through the re-deployment of fifty thousand men to work on repairing the bomb damaged Ruhr, whilst others were seconded to work on the steel and concrete installations that were needed for the flying bombs that were to be targeted on London. The main defensive force protecting the Normandy coastline in 1943 was the Wermacht, which was supplied with old and obsolete equipment.

The British were desperate to fool the Germans that the port of Pas de Calais rather than Normandy was to be the invasion point. Dummy raids were performed at this port and the surrounding area, but Hitler was not duped. He decided to entrust the task of defending the whole of northern France to Field Marshall Erwin Rommel, undoubtedly one of the most charismatic and gifted military men of the War. Rommel's first job was to carry out a detailed inspection of the French towns and coastline to assess the level of existing defensive fortifications. To his horror he discovered that the Atlantic wall was in poor condition in places, and unfinished in others. An additional problem was thrust upon him, for he had been given poorly equipped troops, many of whom were weary from the brutal and heavy fighting on the Russian Front. In a further meeting with Hitler, Romell finally managed to persuade him that he should be given a free hand to prepare Normandy to his own specifications. Initially he was hampered in his efforts by some of the leaders of the divisions that were supposedly there to help him, and although the resources were desperately low and the forces less than well equipped, the majority of his staffs' efforts were poured into the mouth of the Seine and Normandy.

The German's first defensive task was to flood selected sections of land surrounding the beaches. Breaking banks or damming rivers achieved this. It was here that many of the men of the invading force lost their lives through drowning, being dragged below the water by their heavy packs following a parachute landing. There was a huge build up of weed in these flooded areas that was almost impossible to see in the photographs obtained from reconnaissance from the air. Thirty-two fortified areas were erected between the River Vire and Port-en-Bessin. Other stretches of the coast were more than well provided with natural defences such as reefs.

The primary defences however were focused on the French beaches, and in April 1944 the Germans started to construct a system of elaborate obstacles to be placed between the low and high water marks. The first line of defence was a series of Element C structures, or gates, comprised of reinforced iron frames with iron supports, sited on rollers and positioned approximately 250 yards (230m) away from the line of high water. Waterproof 'Teller' mines were attached to the uprights of the main support girders.

The second line, 20 to 25 yards (18-23m) land-wards, consisted of heavy logs driven into the sand with their mine tipped ends arranged to point seawards. The final row was sited about 150 yards (135m) from the shoreline and made of steel rails, 5½ feet (1.6m) in length, formed in the shape of a cross and sited so as to pierce the bottom of incoming craft.

The lines were not continuous, but positioned at irregular intervals. There were no mines in the tidal sands, but they were used to great effect beyond the shingle areas of the beaches. A concertina wire was laid on the top of the Atlantic Wall near the sandy areas, whilst other deadly forms of defence, including charges of TNT covered by rocks and set off by trip wires, ordinary trip wire mines and mustard pots, were set in other vulnerable places.

The Germans concentrated their positioning of land-based fire to protect against a possible oncoming attack from the sea. There was flanking fire positioned on both sides of each beach, with individual strong points consisting of a complex combination of pill-boxes, gun casements, open gun positions and trenches; all of which were protected by mines. There was an elaborate, direct communication between the different components of the defence, achieved via underground quarters, trenches or tunnels.

The majority of the fire was from machine guns, with additional light artillery pieces of various kinds ranging from 75-85 millimetre guns in place. The pill boxes were occupied by lighter guns and anti tank guns, with lateral fire provided by heavier guns. The flashes from the guns were protected by the concrete walls, which made them difficult to see from the sea and the landing sites. Mortar positions were sometimes included in the strong points with forty or so rocket pits sited several hundred yards/metres up on the high ground. These were to prove particularly damaging as the fire could reach the attacking personnel and the transport areas, which came under particularly heavy attack. The main defences were concentrated on the beach areas with little evidence of any significant in-depth inland positioning. The German army defending the area generally consisted of one thousand of their own men, supported by forced or dispirited Poles and Russians. In 1944 Rommel's immediate superior, Field Marshall Gerd Von Runstedt eventually had Army Group B at his disposal, this consisting of a huge force including those stationed in Holland and near the Loire.

Arguments over supplies and tactics between Rommel and Runstedt raged on continually. Rommel still strongly believed that Normandy was the proposed site for the invasion, whilst Runstedt was sure that the ports would be hit first. Other indecision arising from disputes over command also consequently benefited the allies.

CHAPTER 4

Hugh Iorys Hughes was born on 16 April 1902 at 4 Garfield Terrace, Garth, an area near Bangor pier, North Wales, to Mr Owen Rowland Hughes and Mrs Mary Catherine Hughes. His father's mother was the daughter of a sea captain from nearby Porth Dinorwig (Y Felinheli), and his paternal grandfather, Hugh Hughes, was a deacon at the Tabernacle chapel, Mayor of Bangor in 1898, and the owner of a draper's shop, called Britannia House, in the High Street. His maternal grandmother Mary Jones was born at Glasfryn Fawr, Clynnog, and claimed descent from Llywarch ap Bran, Lord of Menai. She was a widow when she met William Hughes, a widower originally from the Llŷn peninsula who was also a Deacon at the Tabernacle and a pork butcher who owned a shop near the town clock in Bangor. They married and had one daughter, Mary Catherine, who was called May by the family.

One morning, William Hughes met Hugh Hughes and his young son Owen Roland, and told him that his red-haired daughter would make a more than suitable companion for his youngster. Not long after this event, O.R. and May met again at kindergarten where he was known to have helped with her arithmetic. Some years later, they married and had six children, four boys and two girls.

Iorys's eldest sister Violet was a gifted child and gained a place to study at the University College Bangor. She married and when her husband's health began to fail, they moved to London where she established a 'crammers' for girls before their entry into St Pauls Girls School. Leslie, the next child and eldest son, entered the Army during the Great War by giving a false age, and was wounded in 1918. The third child, Guinever, studied at Bangor University and taught at Penrhos School until her marriage in 1927 to Cyril Fairchild, a keen amateur golfer and twice winner of the Welsh Championship. Hugh Iorys was born next, followed by his two brothers Richard and Siôr, who both served in the R.N.V.R during the Second World War, one in mine sweepers and the other in destroyers and M.T.B.'s.

O.R. Hughes was a keen sailor and always harboured a great desire to go to sea as his grandfather had done before him. However, the pressures of bringing up a family meant that he was to stay in Bangor and run the shop, but he often made up for this by taking his children sailing whenever he could. On one occasion he was cajoled to take them all on a return journey in a half Decker to the Isle of Man. Iorys was only three or four at the time.

Iorys Hughes was a highly-strung boy with sandy curls and a slight stammer, which he disguised by talking slowly. He was educated at the local Preparatory school, then at Friars Grammar School on Ffriddoedd Road, Bangor. Of the four boys he was the only one who worked hard enough to go to University. His main interest was sailing, as it was with all the family, and he became an expert helmsman, returning regularly from university and then London to the Menai Straits to race with his father. At one time or another, due largely to his exceptional skill in assessing tidal currents, he won every prize in each racing class in the treacherous waters off Menai Bridge and Beaumaris, including The Jubilee Cup in 1935.

His first boat called *Venture*, was a beautiful one rater, which he bought in 1930. He then bought *Meryl*, one of the Mersey Mylne One designs, in 1939. Out of ten starts, he won the cup for the best overall results with six firsts, two seconds and two thirds for the second year running. Following the war the races were restarted and on one particular occasion *Meryl*, skippered by Iorys Hughes was the only entrant in the Mylne class, the other boat owners in Liverpool still smarting from the defeats they had sustained in the 1938/39 years. He sold *Meryl* and bought a Fife One design with his brothers Richard (Dickie) and Siôr, and raced her in the Regattas until the death of his father in 1952. Iorys also raced in the London area and the Solent in dinghies and participated in ocean racing with friends. His passion for sailing did not end there though, for he also enjoyed designing yachts and was a member of the Conwy, the Royal Anglesey and the Royal Merseyside Yacht Clubs, the Royal Cruising Club and the Royal Ocean Cruising Club.

After finishing his studies at Friars School, he went on to

Sheffield University where he studied Engineering. On the night before his final examinations, he very nearly withdrew because of the extent of his worry, and it was not until his Professor advised him otherwise that he went ahead to gain a First Class Honours Degree. Following graduation, one of his earliest jobs was to design a bridge in Scotland. He suspected that the contractors for the foundations were using inferior materials. Although only a novice diver himself, he still insisted on diving down to inspect the works and found that the foundations were not to his specifications and ordered the work redone.

Other projects followed including working with Sir E. Owen Williams and Mr Fitzimmons. In 1942, after translating Sir Owen's concept for the concrete arch of the Empire Pool at Wembley into a working possibility, he left to work from new offices at 66, Victoria Street, London. He proceeded to work on, amongst other things, the Hyde Park underpass and the design of the dock in which the *Cutty Sark* now sits. As the *Cutty Sark* was undergoing reconstruction, Iorys Hughes travelled to the Menai Straits at Anglesey, to retrieve the spans from the stricken *H. M. S. Conway*, and transported them to London for use in the dock.

Following the evacuation from Dunkirk, it was clear to Iorys Hughes that special equipment would be required for invading north-west Europe. He tried to enter the navy, but access was refused as he was employed in a reserved occupation. However, on 1 June 1942 Winston Churchill had his staff send a letter to Iorys Hughes requesting him to produce proposals for the design of prototypes for landing piers for what would become the D-Day landings. If accepted, he was to proceed with their construction and testing. The instructions in his brief stated that he should bear in mind that the average gradient of the shallow sand sea bed beaches open to the south-west on the Normandy coast was approximately 1:200. There would be a range of tides from a maximum of 30 feet (9m) on springs with a speed of 4 knots reached by the tide parallel to the beach that it encountered.

Iorys Hughes worked tirelessly over the following weeks and months and produced plans outlining his proposals. His design consisted of a fixed pier and pierhead that comprised of a huge concrete caisson called a HIPPO and a tubular span called a CROC. Three of these immense Hippos, each measuring 200 feet (61m) long, 60 feet (18m) high and weighing 6,000 tons, would be positioned so as to lie in line on the sea bed. These huge structures were to have large metal approach pylons attached to the top of them to which the two Crocs would be attached. The caissons would float when empty and could be towed by tugs to the intended invasion site and then sunk to a specific depth by the controlled entry of water or exiting of air. Iorys Hughes intended that a number of these Hippos be sunk in line and the connection made to the shoreline by the Crocs, which were to be attached via the metal pylons.

The units were to be constructed in Britain, towed across the English Channel, and placed in the best position so as to provide the means of supplying an invading force. He indicated that the piers would be able to carry the heaviest tanks and artillery, be capable of being moved from one assault beach to another as necessary, and be capable of withstanding any summer gales. They would not require full-scale breakwaters.

Iorys Hughes arranged for most of his staff, who were in the Services or Ministries, to join him at his offices in Victoria Street and proceeded with the work in hand. He had acquired extensive knowledge of the shoreline around Conwy and Deganwy in North Wales during his sailing days, and informed his superiors that in his opinion this part of the Welsh coastline would be ideal to build his prototypes. He did not envisage any problems launching the huge components into the Conwy estuary, or towing them to the trial areas when required.

In a copy of the North Wales Weekly News printed after the War, an article indicates that sometime in 1942 a man called to see the editor to 'check up' on chart and timetable information. He also made enquiries about the condition of the estuary at the junction of the river and the sea, and even asked the local people about depths of water at specific points. He did not reveal to them why he wanted this information.

The nature of the work was to be on a huge scale, and meant that the list of prospective contractors was compiled from all parts of the country. Iorys Hughes whittled the list down and a decision was reached that Holloway Bros Ltd of London and Acme welders of Manchester would carry out most of the work. The main priority was that utmost secrecy be maintained and none of the workers, including the management, were to be aware as to what they would be building over the coming months.

On 28 October 1942, a man called West, who was a Holloway's representative, was given the job of arranging a meeting with the Town Clerk of Conwy Borough Council. In his hand he had a letter of introduction from Iorys Hughes stating that a specific section of land at Conwy called the Morfa, an area to the north-west of Conwy quay, would be required. The first task was to perform trial borings on the beach to examine the sub-soil and to calculate the load bearing capacity of the sand. Another part of the plan suggested the expected use of a derelict building known as the Beacons, which Hughes envisaged to be taken over as a storage area and living accommodation for a proportion of the huge numbers of workmen. Iorys Hughes gained the relevant permission from the local council to use the Morfa, Conwy as the construction site and went on to enter into discussions with other contractors with regard to their suitability for the work that was needed. The Clerk of Conwy Town Council was also informed that the work, described as being 'a vital secret and of Prime Minister priority' was expected to begin within two weeks, with two hundred men initially on site, eventually increasing to a total of one thousand.

The primary survey showed that the construction site itself would require an area with a frontage of approximately 1,150 yards (1050m) onto the foreshore in front of the Beacons. The owners of this area, Conwy Town Council, who had previously leased the land to the Conwy (Caernarfonshire) Golf Club, accepted six pounds per annum for the land. Both sides agreed to the relatively small figure as the land in question was very sandy and had little, if any, agricultural value.

Many buildings near Conwy including Bryn Corach and Beechwood Court on the Sychnant Pass Road leading to Penmaenmawr; as well as Ty'n-y-coed and Plas Mariandir in

Llanrhos, which were both holiday homes, were set aside as hostels to accommodate the workmen. On 30 October 1942, Captain Coulson of the War Department accompanied Iorys Hughes to Conwy. They provided members of the local council with a plan showing additional land, amounting to some ten acres, that was required on the Morfa site fronting Deganwy. It was proposed that an additional part of land that was leased to the Caernarfonshire Conwy Golf Club, close to where the ninth hole was then situated and where the second hole presently sits, would also be required. The work was to commence on 2 November 1942.

As there was not a suitable means of moving raw materials between the main road, the railway lines and the Morfa site, it was necessary to create a new road. The responsibility of constructing The Burmah Road, as local people called it, was that of Conwy Town Council who acted on behalf of Holloway Brothers. Discussions were also held at this stage between the local authorities and the engineers, so that a contract could be drawn up to transport vehicles across the historic Conwy suspension bridge.

Les Derbyshire, one of the site workers now living in Barmouth, recollects that the majority of the working force comprised of men who were either too young or too old for military service. The catchment area for workers ranged as far afield as Bagillt, Prestatyn, Nefyn, Pwllheli and Blaenau Ffestiniog. All the men were led to believe that they were constructing some type of block ships that were to be scuttled at the entrances of crucial harbours or important navigable rivers. Les Derbyshire's first job was to erect shuttering for what, although he did not know it at the time, were the Hippo caissons. When this particular task was completed he was then told to join a squad of joiners and carpenters who were laying the slipway to the Conwy river. The enormous components were to run over the slipways, which were laid on concrete foundations that had been set at intervals down to the river's low water mark.

Les recalled an incident from the early stages of construction when a difference of opinion over the on site transport facilities arose between the management and workers. During one particular lunch hour, all the carpenters were gathered together in

Hugh Iorys Hughes was born 16 April, 1902 in 4 Garfield Terrace, Garth, Bangor in North Wales. He was one of the most eminent civil engineers of the World War II era and recruited to work on the Mulberry Harbours. He worked tirelessly throughout the War period; initially designing, building and testing prototypes, and later he continued to give advice with regard to all aspects of the Harbours, which were to prove so successful in the winning of the War.

THE HARBOUR

by A. P. Herbert.

We saw them come down the river, the comical,
     secret floats,
  Weird shaped like a mad-man's plaything -
     and what could the monsters be!
Were they bridges, docks, or jetties? Were
     they ferries, or forts, or boats?
We held our peace and we wondered, and
     they quietly passed to sea.

But now I have seen the weird shapes made
     one in a work of art.
  I have seen the incredible harbour the
     British have brought to birth.
The puzzle-toy is complete now, each mad
     piece playing a part.
  And this, I saw, is a wonder that never
     was matched on earth.

It was built in the open Channel, it was
     built on a hostile shore,
  It was built in the filthy weather, it was
     built in a nasty blow,
But it lies as neat as a jig-saw set out on
     a nursery floor,
  And it feeds the conquering armies where-
     ever the armies go.

Give thanks for the wild inventors, give thanks
     for the fearless wits
  Who set themselves to a riddle that never
     was put before.
Give thanks for the faultless seamen who
     ferried the crazy bits
  And fashioned a mighty harbour in storm
     on a hostile shore.

Harold Hickling
Rear Admiral
N.O.i.c. Mulberry "B"

*The Harbour, a poem dedicated to the Mulberry Harbours,
written by A.P. Herbert and signed by Rear Admiral Harold Hickling;
Naval Officer in charge of the Mulberry Harbour.*

View to The Vardre, Deganwy, through the metal spans positioned on the top of the Iorys Hughes designed prototype Hippo Caisson.

Completed spans of the Hippo Caisson onto which the Croc Roadway would be attached.

A Hippo Caisson, which could be lowered or raised by the adding or exiting of water, under construction on the Conwy Morfa site.

A completed 6,000 ton Hippo Caisson before launching. The Beacons, the building in the distance, was used for equipment storage and offices.

The launch of Hippo number 1 from the Conwy Morfa.

Partially sunken Hippo caisson lying off the Conwy Morfa with a view of some of the fourteen launching runways on the beach, none of which now remain. A Hippo unit moored off the Conwy Morfa Beach. 12 noon, Sunday, 9 March, 1943.

A Hippo unit moored off the Conwy Morfa Beach. 12 noon, Sunday, 9 March, 1943.

*Towing of the 6,000-ton Hippo caisson from Conwy
for trials in Southwest Scotland.*

*Construction work dated March 1942 on the Croc 1 unit, which was to form one of the
roadways over which vehicles would travel. The present third hole of Conwy
(Caernarvonshire) Golf Club is in the distance.*

*Preparation for launching of the Croc 1 unit
from the Conwy Morfa construction site.*

*A Croc unit roadway unit ready for transportation to Scotland
for trials. The Great Orme, Llandudno stands out behind.*

Towing of the Hippo units by tugs in Cairnhead, Garlieston,
Scotland ready for the addition of the Croc roadways.

Two views of the completed Iorys Hughes design. The caissons fully lowered into the water with the Croc road units in position.

*A view along the Croc roadway
positioned on the sunken Hippo caissons.*

*Trial tests in the open sea of the three Hippo units
connected by the two Croc roadway spans.*

One of the Pierheads constructed in Conwy, which were to be used in the Mulberry Harbours in Northern France. Each of the units supported by four Spud legs. Supply ships were able to moor alongside the Pierheads and discharge personnel and supplies.

Movement of a Pierhead from Conwy to southwest England and then onto France.

Models of completed Mulberry Harbours

*Section of the towing link showing the shore ramp float
complete with boats and tackle ready for shore anchoring.*

*View of the Iorys Hughes modified Hippo (Phoenix) Caissons
forming the harbour wall from the inner side
indicating the protection provided from the waves.*

View of the Pontoon Pierhead model from the shore showing the shore ramp and the floating bridge.

View of static model of the Stores Pierhead showing the discharge of stores from cargo vessels.

A display of the main units forming the Mulberry Harbours equipment, consisting of one A.1 Caisson, one Pontoon or Pierhead, one Concrete Pontoon, one Buffer Pontoon, one Shore Ramp Float, Spans, Floats and a Mooring Shuttle. The picture in the background is that of the Normandy beaches

The Commemorative stone laid at the Conwy Morfa site.

MAE'R MAEN HWN YN COFFAU UN OR CYFRINACHAU
A GADWYD ORAU YN YSTOD RHYFEL 1939-45.
AR Y SAFLE HWN, ADEILADWYD A LANSIWYD I R
AFON CONWY, RANNAU CONCRID HARBWR MULBERRY,
SEF ADEILADWAITH HARBWR GYMLETH A ALLAI NOFIO.
DEFNYDDIWYD EF YN YSTOD Y GLANIO AR DRAETHAU
NORMANDI AR FEHEFIN 6, 1944.

THIS STONE COMMEMORATES ONE OF THE BEST
KEPT SECRETS OF WORLD WAR II. IT WAS ON
THIS SITE THAT CONCRETE SECTIONS OF THE
MULBERRY HARBOUR, A COMPLEX FLOATING
HARBOUR INSTALLATION, WHICH WAS USED FOR THE
NORMANDY D DAY OPERATIONS ON JUNE 6TH, 1944
WERE CONSTRUCTED AND LAUNCHED INTO THE
RIVER CONWY. THE ORIGINAL PROTOTYPE UNITS
WERE DESIGNED BY H.IORYS HUGHES. Esq. M. Eng
F.Inst.C.E. F.Inst.St.E. of BANGOR CAERNARFONSHIRE

*The bilingual tribute to the work carried out during World War II
at the Conwy Morfa.*

The remains of the Phoenix units at Arromanche, Northern France, 2001.

Visitors to the
EXPOSITION PERMANENTE DU DEBARQUEMENT
at Arromanche, the museum dedicated to the D-Day landings and the Mulberry
Harbours, have a clear view of the remaining units
at the Mulberry Harbour site.

the canteen to elect a shop steward to represent them. The man they chose, Mr Vickers from the Prestatyn area, was grateful for the honour of being chosen as their representative and, following the meeting with his 'members', it was proposed that he should approach the management to remedy the situation. Matters dragged on throughout the afternoon and, with valuable time being lost, the management conceded that the problem should be resolved. Not surprisingly a few weeks later Vickers was not seen anywhere on site, something he had earlier predicted.

Raymond Hughes, now living in Chapel Street, Conwy was only fourteen when he was chosen by a 'government man' who visited the Central School (later Cadnant School) in Conwy to work on the construction site. His first job was to wash the pots in the kitchen of the Beacons, which at the time was owned by Arthur Jones. He was then moved to the stores where he handed out the welding tools and gloves and went on from there to carry the welding rods to the welders, who were mostly from London. He recalls delivering the men's registered mail to the local post office, and remembers lorry loads of grease being delivered to be used on the slipways before launching. Hughes also recalled a local haulier called Jim Chalcroft, then of Cadnant Park, transporting items such as nuts and bolts to the construction site in his dark blue Bedford lorry from a siding in the goods yard in Conwy. The work continued over 12-hours a day and Hughes worked a 6-day week.

Mr Ken Hughes, known locally as Ken Rimmer, who still lives in Conwy and sixteen at the time, recalls transporting materials such as planks and pipes from Deganwy Dock to the Morfa. He later took the workmen to the by then floating caissons in a passenger boat owned by Sam Craven. A telephone message was received by the Harbour Master stating that the first of the three Hippo barges were to be launched on 4 May 1943 at 12.10 p.m. and that it would be necessary for the harbour to be closed to all navigation on that date. Before the launch Iorys Hughes added his own racing flag in addition to the Union Jack on the caisson and when asked by the War Office about this, he commented 'Oh, that is my racing flag, it has brought me luck in the past and I hope it will today'. When he told the War Office that they must have a spring tide they said 'But we can't wait for the spring'!

On 18 June 1943, Mr West of Holloway Brothers made it clear that 'he expected to complete all the works on the land adjacent to the Beacons and to clear all materials by next week.' Local people recall that the expected mini-tidal wave that was expected on the opposite shore at Deganwy, did not in fact occur, even though sandbags had been placed outside the entrances to the houses.

The three Hippo concrete caissons and two Croc roadways were finished on time ready for trials at a site to be chosen by Bruce White and his team. There were to be two other designs, one from the Royal Navy Directorate of Miscellaneous Weapon Development (DMWD), an unit that consisted of a number of scientific men from both service and civilian life. In early 1942 DMWD came across Ronald Hamilton, an inventor who had set up his own laboratory in a wing of the bomb-damaged Grosvenor Hotel. Having been asked by DMWD for his observations, he explained that his plan was based on a principle of displacement. In his laboratory he had built a 200ft (61m) water tank in which floated a miniature roadway made of strips of wood and canvas anchored in front and behind by wires. Hamilton was immediately brought onto the DMWD staff as a consulting engineer and his design was christened Swiss Roll, which it resembled when rolled up.

The third design, produced by Tn5 itself, consisted of a floating bridge cum- pierhead. The pierhead was to be fitted with legs to enable it to float up and down with the changes in tide. The spans of the bridge, that were both of fixed and telescopic lengths, were designed by W.T. Everall of the Number 2 Railway Training Centre at Derby. They were to be of a mild steel construction and varying in length from 71 to 80 feet (22m to 24m) and each weighing 28 tons. Spherical bearings would allow the spans, which were to be supported by floats, to twist with the waves. Each of the floats that supported the spans would need to support 56 tons, and an additional weight of up to 25 tons for a tank had to be taken into consideration. These, essentially, had to be cheap and massed produced for it was calculated that a total of four hundred and sixty would be required for the Mulberries. Everall had originally designed a steel float but, with little steel being available, it was decided that concrete would have to be used as an alternative. The company of Mouchel and Partners constructed of what came to bear the codename *Beetles*.

The pierhead itself was adapted from a dredger designed by Henry Lobnitz, but had four spud legs rather than the three that were on the original. The pierhead would be able to move up and down on the spuds, that were in turn run by electrically driven winches.

Bruce White studied the three designs but could not choose which one was best suited to the task in hand. He decided that all the prototypes should be tested and that the three designers be informed as to where this would be done.

CHAPTER 5

All three Mulberry Harbour designs were completed on time and were ready for testing. The military planners and team of engineers now had to find a suitable place to test the Iorys Hughes, War Office and the D.M.W.D. prototypes. The basic requirements posed questions that were difficult to solve. The coastline would need to be made of flat sandy beaches like those on the northern coast of France, and the surrounding area would have to be sparsely populated so as to avoid security risks. The whole of the British coastline was surveyed in a relatively short period of time and the decision reached that the area on and around the Solway coast of south-west Scotland, close to Wigtown Bay, would be ideal for the task in hand. The beaches were flat and sandy, and the nearby harbour at Garlieston considered more than adequate to accommodate all the design components. The fact that the area was sparsely populated was an additional and very important bonus. Following the completion of the Hughes prototype components, they were transported by sea for trials at Rigg Bay at Garlieston on the south-west coast of Scotland.

The work started in earnest and a military camp was built at nearby Cairnhead to house the increasing numbers of engineering personnel, or Sappers as they were called, who would congregate in the area over the following weeks. There was also over-spill accommodation provided for more than two hundred men in the village hall in Garlieston.

The whole of the area from Garlieston to the Isle of Whithorn was placed out of bounds to all but the local fishermen and the roads were regularly patrolled by military police. In 1943, Tn5 formed a unit of Royal Engineers that was placed under the command of Major J. Carline. It was their responsibility to develop and train staff in the use of the Mulberry prototype piers and jetties.

The three Hippo Caissons, enormous as they were, were to be towed by tugs all the way from Conwy to the site at Garlieston. They had to travel via Benllech in Anglesey (Ynys Môn) and then to the River Mersey before starting the long journey north to their position in Rigg Bay. Iorys Hughes subsequently spent many weeks at the trial site where he tested his prototypes. The two Croc roadways were attached onto the metal spans of the Hippos and the combination was tested in a variety of weather conditions. Vehicles of different sizes were driven across the Crocs in both calm and rough waters. Problems were encountered with his construction in that the piers did not rise and fall as expected with the tide, but Iorys Hughes reworked his design and submitted an alternative proposal that had adjustable approach spans, which he proposed would overcome the problem. The trials continued and various other adjustments were made to the prototype design. The biggest problem arose when it was found that the Hippos were liable to become unstable due to the scouring action of salt-water washing around them, and this caused them to list with inevitable buckling of the Croc roadways. To overcome this hurdle, Iorys Hughes suggested constructing Hippos of diminishing size landwards on which the Croc roadways would sit. Sappers from the Royal Engineers (933) made the preparations for this combination. They constructed a base made from solid stone on the shore at Rigg Bay onto which the landward Hippo would be held above the high water mark.

As the Hughes prototype was being tested, the other two prototypes were being assembled. The testing area around Cairnhead had been prepared for the Swiss Roll system and the roadway units were towed there by tugs. The 200 foot (61m) swiss roll units were unloaded and towed across Garlieston harbour early one morning. One of the local residents Mr William Drynan, who still lives in Garlieston, recalls awakening one morning to see men apparently walking on the water as he opened the curtains. They were in fact walking on the Swiss-Roll, the window frame having blocked Mr Drynan's view of the roll itself.

A roadway leading down to the high water mark was built by joining the units together to form overall lengths of 1,500 feet (450m). Ronald and Peter Hamilton arrived on site in July and a series of tests were started. On 5 August, a three-ton Thorneycroft Tipper Truck was driven over the Swiss Roll road but it sank in just over ninety minutes. Adjustments were made and additional trials carried out in the open sea, but the heaviest load that the rolls were capable of bringing ashore was 7 tons. This relatively low bearing capacity ruled out transporting tanks over the Swiss Roll and the design was abandoned.

The Beetles or floats for the Tn5 design, which were a combination of both concrete and steel, were built at Barrow and transported to Garlieston. They were bolted together to form complete units, with the six steel roadway spans arriving on site transported by L.C.T.s. Progress reports indicated that the spans were to be placed on the Beetles on 12 March 1943, but the work was much delayed or even stopped due to harsh weather.

The biggest problem with the Tn5 design was associated with the method of mooring the units. Iorys Hughes had previously outlined this, leading to the development of a kite anchor device by Beckett. Trials were undertaken in relation to the laying operation, and involved the curiously named *slug* boats, slug being an acronym for *Surf Landing Under Girder*. They were used for mooring the floats and the floating roadway.

On 8 April a spud pontoon known as *Winnie* was launched and arrived under tow at Cairnhead on 22 April. It lay there until the poor weather subsided on 17 May, and was then connected to the pier. Three weeks after this date there was to be a full trial in the severest of weather. Although the winds reached speeds up to 60 miles (100km) per hour and the waves reached up to 12 feet (3.6m), a drifter from the 467 Motor Boat Company RASC was successfully driven ashore along the roadway, with only a few bolts in the decking breaking loose. The pier survived intact.

During the first half of 1943 there was close contact between the engineers performing the trials in Scotland and Brigadier Bruce White of Tn5, who often visited the site to see how things were proceeding. Two or three hours before the British delegation flew off to the Ottawa conference that was to decide upon which of the designs would be used, Iorys Hughes was asked to submit an 'appreciation' of his design. The short time allotted to him only allowed him to give a brief description of his Hippo and Croc plan. He was unaware that the final decision upon which design was to be used, would be made in Canada. He was not represented at the conference and was not informed for some time that the War Office (Tn5) design was considered the best option.

The trials in Scotland continued and it was obvious to all that the type of ferocious weather encountered there could easily be encountered in France. As a consequence of this, a decision was reached that some form of Breakwater had to be supplied to protect the Mulberries. Iorys Hughes was kept on as a consultant and during his investigations into the Tn5 design found that there were difficulties associated with it. He proposed that modified Hippo units should be constructed to form the breakwater units which could be used to protect the War Office floating piers. His drawings for using the modified Hippo units as breakwaters were delivered by hand to the War Office. When he later asked for their return, he was told that they had been mislaid and never saw them again.

A final combination of Breakwaters was decided upon and comprised of three units. The first of these and closest to the pierheads, was to consist of fifty-nine obsolete merchant and naval vessels, sunk in line to form a defence against the waves. The vessels were to be amassed at Oban and stripped, ballasted and then fitted with explosives and sailed to France under their own steam. The charges would be exploded on arrival and the ships sunk in place. This defensive line was code-named *Gooseberries*. The next breakwater proposed was a line of concrete caissons, called *Phoenix*. These were to be towed across the Channel, positioned and gradually sunk by adding water. The third component consisted of a floating breakwater code named *Bombardon* positioned further out to sea than the phoenix and gooseberry units, which was a design based on the Lochner Li-Lo design, but in the form of a large metal crucifix.

Hugh Iorys Hughes was informed of the breakwaters that were to be constructed and was asked again for his opinions. He then referred back to his earlier suggestion of using the modified Hippo units. Many other consulting engineers were now brought in to submit proposals for breakwaters, with Iorys Hughes retained to advise on the merits of each.

He was to learn that the War Office Breakwater unit that was chosen had an unmistakable resemblance to the original Hippo units he had built in Conwy, and later tested in Scotland. Even the details of construction, the dimensions, the tonnage, and the methods of handling and sinking were similar. Again he was asked to continue and again he readily offered his services, but on what had transpired to be a rival, and in his opinion, inferior scheme. Indeed, an entry in his personal diary confirms that Bruce White did actually tell him that it was his design that would be used for the breakwaters:

Wed 26.   Called at W/O & saw Wakefield & B. White. Discussed my fees. B.White says Hippos to be used.......

Earlier, whilst working on his Hippo caisson design, Hughes received permission to engage the National Physical Laboratory at their Teddington Tank to look into problems concerning wave action. When the other breakwater plans were submitted he was in attendance and reported on the test conducted. None of the new designs were adopted, and the one that was chosen was a modification of his own Hippo. His recommendations on methods of anchoring the caisson units were also adopted.

CHAPTER 6

The decision upon the actual design of the Mulberry Harbours immediately set a huge construction task into operation. The work began in earnest in December 1943, leaving little more than six months for completion. It was calculated that thirty thousand workers would be required for the work and inducements such as cheap or even free accommodation as well as travelling allowances were offered to those willing to work in London. Ernest Bevin, Minister of Labour, helped smooth over relations with the unions and ensured that personnel was put to its best use. Inside sixteen weeks, twenty-five thousand men had been transferred to the many Mulberry construction sites around the country, and the numbers reached as many as forty-five thousand at the peak of production. The initial order for 4 miles (6.5km) of floating pier and six spud pierheads (code named *Whales*) was found to be inadequate and the revised calculation increased the figures to 10 miles (16km), three of which were spares, and twenty-three pierheads, eight of which were spares. A total of 60,000 tons of steel was required.

The war effort was in full flow and the building industry was stretched to its limits even before the order came through for the extra building sites that were needed around the country. Because many of the skilled staff was at war, or already employed on other projects, personnel that would not normally be associated with the construction business, including tailors and barbers, were drafted in and trained in building work.

A serious problem was the lack of readily available sites to build the two hundred and ten concrete caissons, or *Phoenix* units, which ranged in size from 1,672 to 6,044 tons each. The solution was to construct various dry docks around the coast, the majority of which were built on the banks of the River Thames in London and on the Clyde in Scotland. The steel beetle floats used to stabilise the roadways were assembled at Richborough in Kent and those of concrete built in other parts of the country including Southsea, Marchwood and Southampton. Much of this work was undertaken by Sappers, and their were work would continue in

France once the assault troops managed to secure the Normandy coast.

As the construction work forged ahead, the trials continued in Scotland. One major problem that had to be overcome was to find a means of connecting the blunt end of the roadway to the actual beach. To discharge vehicles safely onto the beach, it was necessary to design a special approach span, known as a Buffer Pontoon. This was a steel ramp, rising from a minimum of 6 inches (15cm) to 7 feet (2.1m) at the point of connection to the span. Trials of the new component were carried out at Rigg Bay in the early months of 1944, the result being that vehicles could now drive directly onto the beach. Other tests performed in Scotland revealed that the Landing Craft for Tanks were able to travel along the pier and run down the buffer pontoon, open its gates and thus allow the vehicles to disembark immediately.

The Morfa area near Conwy, where the Iorys Hughes prototypes had been built, was chosen as one of the many sites for assembling the pierheads and buffer pontoons. An engineering company from Northwich, Joseph Parkes and Sons was chosen as the main constructor. Major H.B. Denton purchased the firm of Joseph Parkes and Sons shortly after the end of the First World War. He was born in 1884 and in his early school years, he showed a particular aptitude for mechanics. When he finished school, his father found him a position as an apprentice to a local firm of engineers, Messrs. Davy Paxman & Company. Whilst there he showed a particular flair for his work and following five successful years apprenticeship, he looked for another firm to better utilise his talents. At the time the firm of Edward Wood & Co. in Salford was looking for sales staff and, in 1907, Denton took up his position in the office. He worked hard and, having gained the attention of Sir Edward Graham Wood, was appointed to the position of joint head salesman. A short time later he was given the sole responsibility for sales and made the acquaintance of John Briggs, another member of staff at Woods. The two worked on some joint ventures, eventually became firm friends and finally business associates. W.K. Dawson and C.J. Lewis who also worked for Woods joined the two and they were to form the nucleus of

H.B. Denton's staff when he formed his own company.

The First World War interrupted the career of the associates. Denton served with the Lancashire Fusiliers, then the Royal Engineers and finally the Royal Flying Corps. After the War he returned to Wood's where he found W.K. Dawson in charge of the production of paravanes. Major Denton as he now was decided to remain a freelance with the view to setting up his own business when a suitable opportunity arose. John Parkes was anxious to dispose of his boiler and steel works and Denton struck a deal in the summer of 1919. The firm prospered between 1919 and 1939 and began producing tank transporters and other war accessories during the Second World War. However, the appointment to build the Mulberry components was the company's greatest wartime achievement.

The firm received its orders in August 1943 to construct and launch six pierheads, or pontoons as they were called. The plans described each unit as being 200 feet (61m) long with a beam of 60 feet (18.2m) and a depth of 10 feet (3m). The pierheads/pontoons were supported by four spud columns, or legs, of heavily welded construction, which could be lowered or raised to and from the seabed, as required, by electrically driven winches. Supply ships would also be capable of tying up alongside the pontoons to discharge onto vehicles that could travel along the roadways to and from the French beaches.

The pontoons would actually be built at the Northwich factory in a prefabricated form of an all welded construction, and then transported to the final assembly point at the Morfa site at Conwy. All the facilities that Iorys Hughes had at his disposal to construct his prototypes, including the construction site and the slipways, were once again put to special use.

A.K. Wilson, an experienced engineer previously apprenticed to the firm of Cleghorn and Bates in Northwich, was in charge of the assembly site. Each pontoon was to weigh 1,000 tons and be complete with oil storage tanks, electrical generating equipment, sleeping and mess accommodation for crews; and also include supplies of bedding, iron rations, first-aid equipment, life-rafts, signal rockets and light anti-aircraft guns.

Mr Ben Williams, now in his late eighties and living in Northwich, was a member of the Parkes work force in the latter part of August 1943. He clearly recalls that after Churchill and Roosevelt had reached an agreement at the Ottawa Conference, the project was to be completed in six to eight months. Williams was a time served template maker with Parkes and it was his job to set out the transverse girders and longitudinal ties, which internally stiffened the box-like pierheads. The work had started on the Monday morning immediately after the second front agreement, but was stopped suddenly in the afternoon. The internal members of the pierheads were not connecting at the correct angle to the end bulkhead. There was considerable panic when it was thought that firms making the same components in other parts of the country would encounter the same problem. An immediate decision had to be made. Ten minutes after the Drawing Office had been alerted to the problem an entourage of designers, draughtsmen and technical people headed by Major H.B. Denton himself invaded the template shop.

Ben Williams explained the situation upon which Denton reached a quick decision and instructed Williams to 'Carry on with *our* angle elevation'. He then instructed Chief Designer C Kirk to circulate by letter 'all other firms involved immediately as to our decision'.

The success of the venture relied on the work being completed by the beginning of May, 1944 and was only achieved by a huge effort both at Conwy and Northwich with both sets of personnel working throughout all the days that were available to them. The secrecy element of the work had been keenly stressed and was accordingly adhered to. The nine hundred or more men that were involved successfully launched the third pierhead in only eighteen days from laying the keel; a truly remarkable feat and a true reflection of the great achievement.

Mr Fred Shingles of Llandudno Junction was 16 or 17 when he started as an apprentice with Joseph Parkes, his father having been Transport Manager for the firm. He worked on the pierheads and remembers that the units, measuring 180 feet (55m) by 12 feet (3.6m) high with a flange of 3 inches (7.6cm), were made of steel that was mainly supplied from the Brymbo Steel Works in Wrexham. He recalls that they had to overcome problems that were associated with the welding, which caused some buckling over long lengths. It was found that if the welders worked from opposite ends and met in the middle, then the problem did not occur.

In order to meet the delivery deadline, five complete pontoons were built and launched at the Conwy Morfa site. Another contribution from Conwy was the building and launching of the four buffer pontoons under the command of Oleg Kerensky, the contractors for these being Waring and Co. Many of the men working on the Morfa site suffered considerably from strain due to the long hours spent welding. Even blackout requirements were ignored on occasions, so great was the urgency. Even so, not one of the men was actually aware of what they were working on.

The six pierheads and four buffer pontoons were now ready to be transferred to assembly points on the south coast of England prior to the invasion. Many other companies were involved in the mass construction and transfer of the Mulberry constituents to the final assembly points, including amongst others; Balfour Beatty, Pauling, Bovis, Laing, Taylor Woodrow, Mowlem and Melville Dundas.

Once again Iorys Hughes was asked to advise on the project and, in particular, where the components should be parked on the south coast of England. Here he had many meetings with the War Office planners and following considerable discussions, Selsey and Dungeness were considered ideal. As Hughes was required to provide information quickly, he was required to live at the sites with the army in the few critical weeks before D-Day.

On 10 February 1944 Hughes received a letter from the War Office thanking him for his recent letter, in which he had supplied results of the model tests at Teddington, including calculations relating to the size of the holes that would be needed in the sides of the caissons to allow for a quick release of water. The letter went on to refer to the hard work that Hughes had carried out on the effect of waves on the units; and the sliding calculations he had performed, obtained from using a friction-less rig at the National

Physical Laboratory. He was also asked to consider how to reduce the sinking times for the caissons, that including blowing off 12-inch square (30cm) holes at any stage of the siting programme. A further letter dated 17 February 1944 from J.A.S. Rolfe to Lt-Col J.G. Carline at the Cairnhead Camp, Isle of Whithorn suggested, upon Hughes's recommendation, that samples of sand be taken from the seabed for analysis in relation to sinking the caissons.

In a letter to Hughes dated 4 March 1944, Major H. G Auduson of The War Office described a programme for the proposed movement of *Phoenix* caissons from the dockyard at Portsmouth, and their sinking for storage at the already surveyed Bramble Bank area. He also suggested that Hughes be present at the trials to study the behaviour of the units and compare them with results achieved with models. A memorandum from Iorys Hughes reflects on a visit made by him, with the Deputy of the Chief of Staff, Captain Gifford R.N and Lt-Cmdr Babb R.N.V.R to a location close to the entrance of the Medway. Here Gifford stated his reservations about the entrance of the site and the possibility of the enemy 'mining in' the units when they were parked. Hughes was of the opinion that the Cant location should be avoided due to its exposure to the east, and that his recommendation of 3 January to use Blythe Sand be given consideration. It was felt that the fewer vessels sunk the less the risk. By adopting a layout as indicated in his accompanying sketch, a minimum of sinking (and pumping) would be achieved. It was not thought this layout would be suitable at Cant owing to the greater exposure of that site.

As late as 18 August 1944 Hughes received letters of gratitude from W.J. Hodge for the sinking tables and graphs he had produced for two *Phoenix* caissons, called Ax and Bx. On 26 October J.S Rolfe asked him for more copies of his drawings (42/1) in connection with his Hippo design. All these letters clearly indicate the continued role that Iorys Hughes played throughout the Mulberry Harbour project with the following quotes from his diary providing further evidence.

Tue 30 called at Dungeness & met Major Balfour - made an inspection of the units (Phoenixes)

Sun 4/6/ Spoke to Wakefield re. cracked units. Told him I had not been afloat in 5. Back to office to input to Carline.

Thurs 8/6 Went aboard A1/40 - listing with leaking bulkheads. Went to A1/1 also leaking.

A1/23 - leaks in bottom - in six cells later repaired and sealed.

A1/29 riddled with holes.

B1/83 - Damaged bottom.

D/142 - Cracked.

There are many references in his diary to other meetings with Brigadier Bruce White to discuss the Mulberry plans in general; with Lt-Col Carline regarding the launching of the caissons, and with Colonel Wakefield of The War Office concerning the operation of the valve openings on the Phoenixes. He spent further weeks at the testing sites dealing with various problems, particularly the methods of mooring the piers that were to remain afloat and have to be held in place by anchors. He was also involved with other groups on discussions about ways of siting the Mulberry Harbours in the shortest possible time.

CHAPTER 7

The first two weeks of the Allied invasion of Europe saw a total of twenty divisions landing on the French coast, and more that one million men were transferred to occupied territory. The German defence was still formidable, but it gradually weakened and was quickly outnumbered. It was however imperative that the Allied fighting forces be supplied and reinforced with armaments, ammunition and food.

The responsibility for building the British Harbour, Mulberry B, was given to No. 1 Port Construction and Repair Group, which was originally formed by Lt.-Col. Stuart Gilbert in September 1942 to operate in North Africa. In February 1944, to his great surprise, he was asked to form a special force. He demanded that his old group be the nucleus for the newly formed 969 & 970 Port Floating Equipment Companies, responsible for the piers and pierheads; and the 930 & 935 Port Construction and Repair Companies. The former was to clear the beach approaches and demolish all obstacles, whilst the latter was to provide crews for the caissons while they were being towed.

On the afternoon of 6 June 1944, with the assault troops established on the French coast, the Mulberry forces were given the order to sail. Lt.-Col Mais was put in overall charge of building the piers, and by the early hours of 7 June outer markers at high water level, and others for alignment purposes on the higher ground inshore, had been established for the first two piers. The responsibility for laying the buoys for the *Phoenix* caissons and block ships for Mulberry B was given to Lt-Cmdr Lansdowne of the Royal Navy. Lt-Cmdr Passmore was placed in charge at the American Harbour, Mulberry A.

On 7 June, block ships were steered from their mooring sites near and around Poole Harbour to France. These formed lines of breakwaters, randomly code named Gooseberries. The scuttling of the ships was not easy and tugs were utilised to overlap the crafts in position to prevent scouring and disintegration by the running seawater. The siting of the first line of block ships, or Gooseberry 1, at the American beach, Utah, proved more difficult than had been expected due to the heavy enemy fire and the rapid dispersal of the tugs that were vulnerable to attack. By good luck, the enemy actually managed to sink the second and third block ships more or less in place. The ships formed two crescent shaped harbours and Gooseberry 1 was completed on the 13th June and accommodated seventy-five Liberty ships and small craft. Gooseberry 2 at Mulberry A was completed three days earlier on the 10th June. Gooseberry 3 was sited at Mulberry B, where one ship was sunk at 90 degrees to the others that resulted in a gap, later filled by a Phoenix caisson. Gooseberry 4 was the shelter for Courseilles, seven miles (11km) east of Arromanche. Gooseberry 5, consisting of nine Block ships, was located off Ouistreham.

The cruciform shaped floating *Bombardon* breakwater units that were to form the outer line of defence against the waves, set sail on 6 June 1944. Their moorings had been laid by boom laying craft and each breakwater measured a mile (1.6km) in length at each Mulberry Harbour. Problems arose with the placing of these units however due to a mistaken order to lay them in a single line, although they had been designed to lie in a double line. They were also erroneously moored at some 11 to 13 fathoms (20m to 24m) rather than the necessary depth of 7 fathoms (13m), making them far less effective in reducing the size of waves.

The towing of the *Phoenix* caissons; each of which was provided with a gun, a four-man crew and two sailors, also began on 7 June 1944. Two *Phoenix* units were positioned at Mulberry A on 10 June, the delay being the result of ferocious enemy fire. By 14 June, thirty-one of the fifty-one caissons had been positioned with only a few floating away. Admiral Hickling was put in charge of Mulberry B and by 18 June, twenty-five of the *Phoenixes* had been sited with only four lost in the assault phase.

The installation of the stores and L.S.T piers proved more difficult than that of the block ships and Bombardons. The tows began to arrive at Mulberry B on 10 June with men working throughout the night to complete the task. The approach spans were placed in position by steam tugs and motor towing launches. Due to the worsening weather and the choppy seas, manoeuvring the bridging into line was difficult, but by 14 June the stores pier east had been laid to a three quarter mile (1.2km) length from the shore with the 'spud' legs attached. Loads could now be discharged from coasters onto the lorries. The second stores pier was completed on 7 July and Sappers had cleared the beach approaches for the shore ramps of mines and other obstacles. The leading tank crossed the centre pier on 16 June but it took until 8 July before the second pier and pierhead were ready. The installation of the L.S.T. piers was delayed due to problems with securing the concrete floats, or *Beetles* as they were called. The construction of the pier at Mulberry A started on 12 June, the delay of three days being caused by heavy sniper fire and the large number of beach obstacles that had been encountered. The *Beetles*, however, were arranged alternately on each side of the piers rather than opposite each other on both sides, and this error proved to be costly later on.

On 16 June the Germans began to launch air attacks on the harbours and on 19 June dropped pressure mines that were designed to detonate from the pressure of waves under the ships when they moved through shallow water. But the beachheads had now been secured and the enemy was outnumbered. The build-up of supplies, and in particular ammunition, was absolutely vital but disaster very nearly struck on 19 June. A cold front that originating over Iceland spread over Britain to combine with a depression from the Mediterranean that produced a north-north-west wind of force 6 to 7. There was also an enormous build up of clouds over the French coastline. The more experienced of the sailors involved in the Mulberry B construction were dubious of the weather reports they had received and insisted on immediate action. They suspected that the pierheads and associated equipment would be easily damaged and that the moorings needed to be doubled without any loss of time. A decision was reached that all shipping on the weather side of the piers should be re-sited to reduce anchor drag on the piers and pierheads, and that the spud legs be extended to their fullest extent. The tugs were stocked with two days rations. They were to be continually manned so as to get a line to any of the bombardons, which may break loose or, alternatively, to sink them.

The order was given at Mulberry B that the immediate priority was to save the stores pier and that those ships other than those discharging should up anchor without delay. On 20 June the waves were 8 feet (2.4m) high and crashing against the pierheads and washing over the floating bridges causing them to buckle under the immense strain. The workmen aboard them were only able to hold on to the sides as best they could. The bad weather continued for four days with a number of the vessels drifting. The probability of loose units colliding increased and on 21 June, a runaway steel float became lodged under one of the stores piers. As each new wave approached, the float crashed again against the steel trusses and smashed against a concrete float causing minor damage. Some men worked heroically to move the float using a line from one of the tugs. The Landing Ship for Tanks (LST) pier, which at the time was only half built, caught the worst of the storm. Girders broke and the telescopic spans split from the bridge. Sappers bulldozed a path to jack up and float off one of the washed up telescopic spans from cliffs nearby. The exposed reinforced bars punctured the buoyancy bags, later replaced by oil drums, cans and ping-pong balls, and tore out the bolts that connected the concrete decks of the floats.

A pair of pierheads was isolated and the pontoons were 'spudded' or raised to their maximum and the red warning lights kept on permanently in case of collision. The pierheads held, however, despite some of the spud legs failing.

Water invaded the Phoenix caissons. Some filled to the brim because the wooden hatches that had been purposely designed to block the holes on the side of the caissons had not been closed. The penstocks at the base of the units were designed to let water in at a controlled rate, but the water could not exit quickly enough. Five of the units split as the pressure increased under 30 feet (9m) head of water as the tide turned. An additional problem was that the scouring action of the water caused one of the Phoenixes to shift. The line of block ships fared a little better because they were positioned on a rocky seabed. Two broke their backs but the rest held firmly in place.

The least protected components of the harbours were the

bombardons, and they began failing because of broken bolt connections. The tugs were kept busy saving those that had broken loose from crashing into the piers. Other casualties included two hundred and fifty small craft, including several Rhino ferries, all of which were sunk or battered on the shore. The motor towing launches were moved continually and survived, whilst other vessels continued to unload despite the storm. White paint on the piers guided the truck drivers during the night hours.

The American harbour site at Mulberry A, however, was totally exposed to the full brunt of the storm. LCT's and other craft struck the moored piers, and much of the structure was poorly moored in any case. Although efforts were concentrated on saving the piers and the pierheads, they were to no avail, as the relentless weather bent and twisted the spans. On 21 June the spuds of the two pierheads broke and the pontoons were washed ashore. The remainder survived only by the pontoon being allowed to move up and down through releasing the unit clutch.

Allied Chiefs of Staff and engineers, however, decided to abandon the Mulberry A after the demise of the Phoenix breakwater. Out of the thirty-one units that had been sited, twenty-one were destroyed. Backs and sides broke under the enormous pressure of water and some were hit by rogue bombardons. Over one hundred craft were lost and discharge was subsequently stopped. Ammunition was then brought in by air and supply ships were beached. As the storm abated the DUKWs and ferries began to operate again; 10,000 tons were unloaded at Omaha beach and the projected output was achieved without the use of the Mulberry Harbour.

The beaches at which the extra Gooseberries had been sited were better protected, although two of the block ships and three others were damaged at Utah beach. As the storm waned it quickly became evident that repairing Mulberry A was out of the question, but there was obvious worth in reinforcing its Gooseberries.

Mulberry B was to be rebuilt to its original plan and strengthened so as to be operable to the end of the year, or to at least until October 1944. The bombardons were not replaced and all the gaps that the storm caused were filled with equipment salvaged from the ill-fated Mulberry A. The Americans had collected spares, and saved as much undamaged equipment as possible and then towed it to Mulberry B at Arromanche. The LST Pier was also repaired and, with the aid of a floating crane, bulldozers, welders and steel erectors, the pier was in operation by 17 July, discharging tanks and other vehicles.

The excess water was let out of the Phoenixes by removing the wooden hatches and drilling holes into their sides. Stronger double-sided units eventually reinforced the breakwaters. Open units were given extra stability by filling them with sand brought from the peninsula of Cherbourg.

In the first two weeks of operations, nearly 27,500 tons of supplies were discharged through both the harbours. The projected supply of 6,000 tons per day was reached on 6 July, with a maximum number of 1,125 vehicles being landed at Mulberry B in one day. It was also found that coasters and landing craft were able to work much more effectively at those beaches that were protected by the Gooseberries, and subsequently achieved much more than was expected of them.

When the Allied forces advanced from the beachhead on to the Seine, it caused an immense strain on the supply system. It was, however, still necessary to depend upon Mulberry B and the Gooseberry protected beaches since the ports of Cherbourg and those of Brittany had been demolished and mined by the departing German forces. Mulberry B at Arromanche was indeed left open until 19 November as it was the only anchorage capable of providing sufficient shelter for the Liberty ships, each of which carried 7,000 tons of supplies. Inclement weather continued to play havoc with the discharge from the harbour during July and August and, in September, the coastline was again pounded by heavy seas. The construction of extra concrete caissons in Britain, to reinforce the harbour, proved vital as improvements had to be made to the breakwater systems. By mid-September an area of 2 square miles (3.2km sq) was enclosed within the harbour, which was capable of berthing seven liberty ships and twenty-three coasters at any one time. The discharge of supplies was at its maximum at the end of July when 136,164 tons of stores went through the harbour. In the second week of August over 10,000 vehicles passed over the LST pier.

CHAPTER 8

The War Office received a bill for the war work from Iorys Hughes, but delayed payment and suggested that he accept a reduced fee. Not wanting to be thought of as a 'war profiteer', Iorys Hughes accepted their proposal. The reduced professional sum he received for his services scarcely covered the cost of his staff and overheads and he finished the War worse off financially than he began it, and three stones lighter in weight!

In the years following the War, people would frequently ask why he had received little recognition for his work on the Mulberry Harbour project. He even came to suspect that his colleagues doubted his contribution and, though a modest man, this caused him considerable concern.

On the 27 February 1967 Iorys Hughes wrote a series of notes in which he stated why he believed he had received no recognition by way of an honour. After the release of the news of the Mulberry Harbour to the press by the admiralty, Brigadier Bruce White of TN5, went and complained to Winston Churchill about the 'other side' stealing what he regarded as his fire. This reflected the perpetual strife that existed between the services. The Prime Minister promised the Brigadier a Knighthood there and then, with no other official honour bestowed at that time. Many civilians laid extravagant claims to having made important contributions to the war effort. Almost every civil engineer contractor employed on building contracts and consultants were similarly engaged to supervise the work. There were, no doubt, innumerable people who had hopes of recognition.

A friend of Iorys Hughes wrote to one of Churchill's secretaries, telling him that if what Iorys Hughes claimed he had done in the War was correct, then he had been shabbily treated. Churchill's man replied that, although his services were worthy of recognition, it had been decided not to give further honours - no doubt due to the vast number aspiring to some reward or other. The only honour given at a later date was to the Director of the Ministry of Supply. He was in control of the contractual side of the operation when the Mulberry Harbour became such a vast undertaking, and he received a knighthood for this service amongst others.

In 1946 Iorys Hughes was asked by Mike Mason, the Commodore of the Royal Ocean Racing Club, to skipper the 72 foot (22m) yawl *Lafita* in the famous Bermuda Race. The crew of eight members crossed the Atlantic and reached New York in four stages, mostly under sail and having encountered severe weather on the voyage. Iorys Hughes was the navigator and proved inspirational to all members of his crew. Officials of the Cruising Club of America greeted them enthusiastically and minor repairs were carried out to *Lafita*. They continued to achieve a very creditable fifth place overall. It was indicative of his sailing skills that, during his time in Bermuda, Iorys Hughes borrowed an international one-design yacht and won the cup that was offered as first prize in a race against the local sailors.

On his return to Britain he married Jane Vernon, whom he had known for some years. He continued to work for many years on different projects from his London offices. Although he was not willing to talk of his own achievements, even to his close family, his wife later revealed that some of his projects included an underground car park at Hyde Park, 'something' in Saville Row (possibly a car park) and the approach to the Blackwall Tunnel.

In 1960 he suffered a heart attack, but made a full recovery. On retiring, he would have loved to have lived in one of the terraced houses fronting the beach at Beaumaris but agreed with his wife to stay close to London. They bought a house in West Mersea in Essex, an area very similar to parts of the north Wales coastline, where he became a well-respected figure and continued his passion for sailing, and joined the local Sailing Club.

Iorys Hughes died in 1977 and received numerous tributes in the press from many sources. His work during the Second World War was much acknowledged. For years, Siôr Hughes had worked tirelessly to have his brother's Mulberry Harbour work recognised. Iorys had not been of much help to him during these years, for he was the most modest of men and of the opinion that it had all happened many years ago, and was a matter of ancient history. Even so, largely due to Siôr Hughes's years of effort to gain some kind of recognition for his reticent brother, Conwy Town Council decided that a celebration of the magnificent work performed on the Morfa, and especifically the huge contribution of Iorys Hughes, should be commissioned.

On 31 May 1978, Sior Hughes received information in a letter from Mrs A. Bitowski of Conwy Town Council that detailed the nature of the resulting parade. The communication proclaimed that it would occur on Tuesday, 6 June 1978 when it was hoped that Siôr Hughes and his wife Rosemary would be able to attend. As usual at such events, many dignitaries were to also attend and the form of the Ceremony was described as follows:

2.30 p.m.	Military Parade from Lancaster Square, Conwy, to the Mulberry Harbour Site on Conwy Morfa.
3.00 p.m.	National Anthem.
3.10 p.m.	The Town Mayor (Councillor R. W. Springfield) will give a speech of welcome.
3.15 p.m.	Hymn: *O God, Our Help in Ages Past*.
3.20 p.m.	Dedication Service by the Mayor's Chaplain, Revd Canon R. Dwyfor Jones, assisted by Revd D. Emrys Jones, Revd O.J. Roberts and Revd Pennant Lewis
3.30 p.m.	Last Post.
3.32 p.m.	Unveiling of Commemorative Stone by Major General A.G.E. Stewart Cox., D.F.C., General Officer Commanding (Wales).
	Reveille
	Hymn: *Abide With Me*

After the Ceremony the dispersal point was to be at the Conwy (Caernarfonshire) Golf Club at approximately 4.15 p.m. where they were invited to take tea with the Town Mayor and Members of the Council.

The 'Conwy Exhibition' of photographs and newspaper cuttings of Iorys Hughes's and Conwy's work was on display from 1.00pm until 4.00pm on the day at the Guildhall, Conwy and to run for a further week. The Band of the Royal Welsh Guards played during the parade and, together with members of local organisations, a contingent of soldiers from the Depot of the Prince of Wales Division, Crickhowell also attended. The Mayor's Chaplain, the Reverend Canon R. Dwyfor Jones, assisted by other clergy of the community, undertook the dedication of the memorial stone. Major General A.G.E Stewart Cox, D.F.C., General Officer Commanding Wales, performed the unveiling of the commemorative stone at the Morfa site. In his address he stated how great an honour it was for him to have been asked to travel from Brecon to unveil the memorial. As he saw it, it was a tribute to the ingenuity and creative brilliance of British Civil and Marine engineers. He proceeded to comment on the small military parade and the strong association between the Welsh people and the fighting services. It was his opinion that all the people involved, engineers, ex-quarrymen, draughts men, labourers, and craftsmen of all kinds, should receive the majority of the praise; and that the parade should have been led by Hugh Iorys Hughes, the distinguished Welsh civil engineer, whose brilliance had converted his visionary ideas and concepts into reality. He praised the quiet, self-effacing man who never sought the limelight and who would probably have refused an invitation to lead the parade even if he had been alive.

He concluded by thanking Iorys Hughes and all those who laboured with him on the Morfa thirty-five years previously for, without their remarkable work, it was his opinion that it would have been questionable whether the Allies, following D-Day, could have been supplied and sustained in France. Major General Cox went as far as to speculate whether the war could have been won without the Mulberry Harbours. He then went on to unveil the memorial.

The Mayor and the Council members were late for the parade because they had been delayed whilst taking guests into the Guildhall to look at the photographs of the Morfa Construction site. The parade set off early and the council dignitaries had to hurry in their ceremonial robes to the unveiling, with the Band of The Welsh Guards being asked to play so as to fill in the embarrassing hiatus.

Shortly after the ceremony Siôr Hughes sent a letter to Stewart

Cox thanking him for his speech, a transcript of which he received in a return letter from Major General Cox.

The commemorative stone originally occupied a place on the Conwy Morfa Car Park facing Deganwy. Some time later it was moved approximately 200 metres inland and a board was installed on which a rather vague version of the wartime events is given. Disappointingly, brambles now surround the commemorative stone and there is little indication that it is there at all these days.

There is no remaining structural evidence of the war effort work that was carried out on the Morfa beach. In the waters off Rigg Bay, west of Garlieston in south-west Scotland, however, stands one of the Hippo's that were built at Conwy, the other two having being towed away many years before and dismantled in Larne, Ireland.

A public house called The Mulberry was opened at the Conwy Marina complex in early 1998. Inside is a collection of photographs of the Morfa site, the Prototype testing area in south-west Scotland and a brief history of the Mulberry project. On entering the establishment a large photograph of Iorys Hughes stands above the others, in its proper place.